A **Literature Kit**™ F O R

The Tale of Despereaux

By Kate DiCamillo

Written by Marie-Helen Goyetche

GRADES 3 – 4

Classroom Complete Press
P.O. Box 19729
San Diego, CA 92159
Tel: 1-800-663-3609 / Fax: 1-800-663-3608
Email: service@classroomcompletepress.com

www.classroomcompletepress.com

ISBN-13: 978-1-55319-326-5
ISBN-10: 1-55319-326-1

© 2007

Critical Thinking Skills

The Tale of Despereaux

Skills For Critical Thinking		1-5	6-10	11-15	16-19	20-23	24-29	30-33	34-40	41-46	47-Coda	Writing Tasks	Graphic Organizers
LEVEL 1 Knowledge	• Identify Story Elements				✓			✓		✓			✓
	• Recall Details	✓	✓	✓	✓	✓	✓	✓	✓	✓	✓	✓	✓
	• Match		✓			✓			✓		✓		
	• Sequence	✓		✓				✓			✓		✓
LEVEL 2 Comprehension	• Compare Characters				✓		✓	✓				✓	✓
	• Summarize								✓	✓	✓	✓	✓
	• State Main Idea				✓		✓	✓					✓
	• Describe	✓			✓		✓					✓	✓
	• Classify								✓				✓
LEVEL 3 Application	• Plan	✓	✓	✓	✓	✓		✓	✓	✓			
	• Interview									✓		✓	✓
	• Identify Outcomes	✓	✓	✓	✓	✓	✓		✓	✓			
LEVEL 4 Analysis	• Draw Conclusions	✓	✓	✓	✓	✓	✓	✓	✓	✓	✓		✓
	• Identify Supporting Evidence	✓	✓	✓					✓				✓
	• Make Inferences	✓	✓	✓	✓	✓				✓			✓
	• Identify Cause & Effect			✓		✓	✓			✓			✓
LEVEL 5 Synthesis	• Predict	✓	✓	✓	✓	✓		✓	✓	✓	✓		
	• Design											✓	
	• Create					✓	✓					✓	
	• Imagine alternatives										✓		✓
LEVEL 6 Evaluation	• Defend An Opinion	✓	✓	✓	✓	✓		✓	✓	✓	✓	✓	
	• Make Judgements			✓		✓	✓	✓	✓				

Based on Bloom's Taxonomy

Contents

TEACHER GUIDE

- Assessment Rubric 4
- How Is Our Literature Kit™ Organized? 5
- Graphic Organizer Transparencies 6
- Bloom's Taxonomy for Reading Comprehension 7
- Teaching Strategies 7
- Summary of the Story 8
- Vocabulary 9

STUDENT HANDOUTS

- Spotlight on Kate DiCamillo 10
- Chapter Questions
  - *Chapters 1 – 5* 11
  - *Chapters 6 – 10* 14
  - *Chapters 11 – 15* 17
  - *Chapters 16 – 19* 20
  - *Chapters 20 – 23* 23
  - *Chapters 24 – 29* 26
  - *Chapters 30 – 33* 29
  - *Chapters 34 – 40* 32
  - *Chapters 41 – 46* 35
  - *Chapter 47 – Coda* 38
- Writing Tasks 41
- Word Search 44
- Comprehension Quiz 45

EASY MARKING™ ANSWER KEY 47

GRAPHIC ORGANIZER TRANSPARENCIES 53

Assessment Rubric

The Tale of Despereaux

Student's Name: _____ Assignment: _____ Level: _____

	Level 1	Level 2	Level 3	Level 4
Comprehension of the Novel	• Demonstrates a limited understanding of the novel	• Demonstrates a basic understanding of the novel	• Demonstrates a good understanding of the novel	• Demonstrates a thorough understanding of the novel
Content	• Information incomplete; key details missing	• Some information complete; details missing	• All required information complete; key details contain some description	• All required information complete; enough description for clarity
Style	• Little variety in word choice; language vague and imprecise	• Some variety in word choice; language somewhat vague and imprecise	• Good variety in word choice; language precise and quite descriptive	• Writer's voice is apparent throughout. Excellent choice of words; precise language.
Conventions	• Errors seriously interfere with the writer's purpose	• Repeated errors in mechanics and usage	• Some errors in convention	• Few errors in convention

STRENGTHS:

WEAKNESSES:

NEXT STEPS:

Teacher Guide

Our resource has been created for ease of use by both TEACHERS and STUDENTS alike.

Introduction

Kate DiCamillo's novel, **The Tale of Despereaux**, is a wonderful fairy tale about a mouse named Despereaux, a wicked rat, Roscuro, and the eternal struggle between good and evil, darkness against light, all with a "happily ever after" ending. A Newbery Medal winner, this is an entertaining and heartening adventure that has become a favorite for both boys and girls alike. The story is written in the gloomy setting of a castle and its dungeon, and as Despereaux's quest unfolds, young readers will want to keep the pages turning in order to find out what will happen next!

How Is Our Literature Kit™ Organized?

STUDENT HANDOUTS

Chapter Activities (in the form of reproducible worksheets) make up the majority of our resource. For each chapter or group of chapters there are BEFORE YOU READ activities and AFTER YOU READ activities.

- The BEFORE YOU READ activities prepare students for reading by setting a purpose for reading. They stimulate background knowledge and experience, and guide students to make connections between what they know and what they will learn. Important concepts and vocabulary from the chapter(s) are also presented.

- The AFTER YOU READ activities check students' comprehension and extend their learning. Students are asked to give thoughtful consideration of the text through creative and evaluative short-answer questions and journal prompts.

Six **Writing Tasks** and three **Graphic Organizers** are included to further develop students' critical thinking and writing skills, and analysis of the text. (*See page 6 for suggestions on using the Graphic Organizers.*) The **Assessment Rubric** (*page 4*) is a useful tool for evaluating students' responses to the Writing Tasks and Graphic Organizers.

PICTURE CUES

Our resource contains three main types of pages, each with a different purpose and use. A **Picture Cue** at the top of each page shows, at a glance, what the page is for.

 Teacher Guide
- Information and tools for the teacher

 Student Handout
- Reproducible worksheets and activities

 Easy Marking™ Answer Key
- Answers for student activities

EASY MARKING™ ANSWER KEY

Marking students' worksheets is fast and easy with our **Answer Key**. Answers are listed in columns – just line up the column with its corresponding worksheet, as shown, and see how every question matches up with its answer!

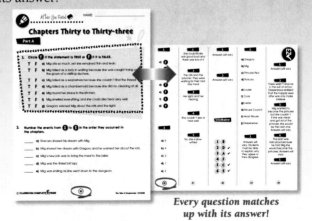

Every question matches up with its answer!

1,2,3
Graphic Organizer Transparencies

The three **Graphic Organizer Transparencies** included in this Literature Kit™ are especially suited to a study of **The Tale of Despereaux**. Below are suggestions for using each organizer in your classroom, or they may be adapted to suit the individual needs of your students. The transparencies can be used on an overhead projector in teacher-led activities, and/or photocopied for use as student worksheets. To evaluate students' responses to any of the organizers, you may wish to use the **Assessment Rubric** (on page 4).

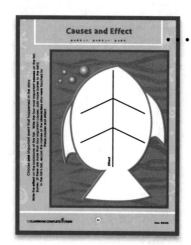

CAUSES AND EFFECT

Students are to choose one important event that happened in the story. Have them write the effect (final outcome) on the backbone of the fish. Then, they identify and record the key causes on the bones of the fish. Some events will have from one to four important causes, while others have more. If there are more than four causes, students can add more bones to the fish. In the tail, write down the names of the characters who are touched by these events. This activity can be used both individually and for group work. Found on Page 53.

WHAT ARE YOU THINKING?

This graphic organizer is a useful tool to help students identify and understand a character's thoughts, feelings and behaviors. Students are to choose one character from the story. Have them write down as many of his or her thoughts, feelings and actions as they can, in the order they happened in the story. Particular attention can be paid to the decisions the character made based on his or her thoughts and feelings. For a follow-up activity, have students write about what might have happened if the character had made different choices. Found on Page 54.

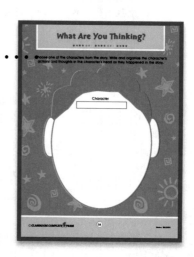

CHARACTER COMPARISON

This graphic organizer is an excellent tool to help students see similarities and differences between characters, and is a good alternative to the traditional Venn diagram. Have students choose two characters from the novel (i.e., Despereaux and Roscuro) and record their names in the center oval. In the top-most box, they are to list ways in which the characters are alike. In the bottom boxes, they are to list ways in which they are different. Students should consider personality traits, thoughts, feelings, actions, the characters' relationships with others, etc. Found on Page 55.

Bloom's Taxonomy* for Reading Comprehension

The activities in this resource engage and build the full range of thinking skills that are essential for students' reading comprehension. Based on the six levels of thinking in Bloom's Taxonomy, questions are given that challenge students to not only recall what they have read, but move beyond this to understand the text through higher-order thinking. By using higher-order skills of application, analysis, synthesis and evaluation, students become active readers, drawing more meaning from the text, and applying and extending their learning in more sophisticated ways.

This Literature Kit™, therefore, is an effective tool for any Language Arts program. Whether it is used in whole or in part, or adapted to meet individual student needs, this resource provides teachers with the important questions to ask, inspiring students' interest, creativity, and promoting meaningful learning.

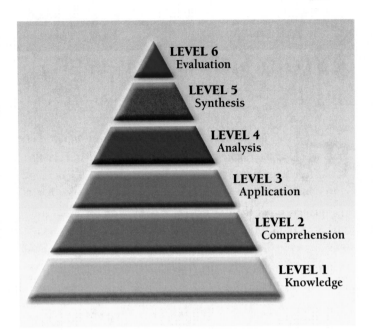

BLOOM'S TAXONOMY: 6 LEVELS OF THINKING

Bloom's Taxonomy is a widely used tool by educators for classifying learning objectives, and is based on the work of Benjamin Bloom.

Teaching Strategies — WHOLE-CLASS, SMALL GROUP AND INDEPENDENT STUDY

The Tale of Despereaux is a novel that may be approached in several ways. Most obvious is as a traditional, whole-class read-aloud in which the teacher reads the book out loud to the entire class, stopping after one or more chapters for the students to answer the chapter questions. As they complete the questions, students reread the chapter(s) on their own. Depending on the interests and needs of your students, you may choose to apply some shared or modeled reading, focusing discussion on the author's skills, choices made in writing, and the elements of the narrative. The BEFORE YOU READ and AFTER YOU READ activities in this Literature Kit™ provide a basis for such discussions.

To facilitate small group and independent study learning, these activities have been divided into chapter groupings to allow students to work on manageable

sections of the novel, and not feel overwhelmed by the activities. Teachers may also choose to use only a selection of the activities in this resource for small group or independent study, assigning tasks that match students' specific needs, and allowing students to work at their own speed. The components of this resource make it flexible and easy to adapt as not all of the activities need to be completed.

Teachers may wish to have their students keep a daily reading log so that they might record their daily progress and reflections. Journaling prompts have been included at the end of each chapter section to facilitate students' thinking and writing.

Summary of the Story

A STORY of an unusual and very special mouse who is on a dangerous quest to rescue a princess.

T his is the story of Despereaux, an unusual and very special mouse who would rather read storybooks than eat them. One day Despereaux falls in love with a princess in the castle in which he lives. Princess Pea is a real princess, but there is a problem – mice and humans are not supposed to talk to each other! After being seen by his fellow mice with the princess, Despereaux is sentenced to the dungeon in order to protect all of the other mice from getting banished from the castle.

Deep down in the dungeon we meet a rat named Roscuro who is fascinated with light. One evening he sneaks upstairs to join a party and finds himself hanging from a chandelier. The worst imaginable thing happens when he falls from the chandelier right into the queen's bowl of soup. The queen is scared to death – literally. As a result of the queen's untimely death, soup and all the utensils needed to make it, along with rats, are all outlawed in the Kingdom of Dor. The king sends his soldiers to scour the kingdom and rid it of all the forbidden items.

Next, we meet an unfortunate young girl, Miggery Sow, who is found by one of the king's soldiers. Miggery's eyesight and hearing are not very good and she is slow witted as well. The soldier brings her back to the castle. Miggery, wanting to become a royal princess at the castle, teams up with Roscuro in hopes of making her dream come true. Roscuro tells her of his plan to capture Princess Pea and take over the castle, and convinces Miggery to join him.

Meanwhile, Despereaux escapes the dungeon and goes looking for his beloved, the princess. The Princess, however, has already been tricked by Roscuro and Miggery, and has been taken to the dungeon. Despereaux must save his love, and together with the help of his friends, eventually rescues her. As his quest comes to a close, Despereaux realizes that he still cannot marry the princess, as princesses do not marry mice. They can, however, become friends. The story ends with the king, the princess, Roscuro, Despereaux, and Miggery Sow all eating soup and living happily together.

Suggestions for Further Reading

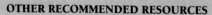

BOOKS BY KATE DICAMILLO

Because of Winn-Dixie © 2000
Tiger Rising © 2001
Mercy Watson to the Rescue © 2005
Mercy Watson Goes for a Ride © 2006
The Miraculous Journey of Edward Tulane © 2006

OTHER RECOMMENDED RESOURCES

E.B. White, *Charlotte's Web* © 1952
Roald Dahl, *James and the Giant Peach* © 1961
Roald Dahl, *The BFG* © 1982
Beverly Cleary, *The Mouse and the Motorcycle* © 1965
Dick King-Smith, *Babe: The Gallant Pig* © 1983
Mary Pope Osborne, *The Knight at Dawn* © 1993

Vocabulary

CHAPTERS 1 TO 5
• diplomat • handkerchief • shard • brilliance • proclaimed • ruin • existence • speculation • obscenely • fainted • demonstrate • scurrying • instructed • scrabbling • squiggles • indignant • dungeon • conform • abandoned • maiden • indulge • instincts • adhere • squinted • executing

CHAPTERS 6 TO 10
• clutched • despair • statement • tribunal • furiously • council • affected • velvet • immediately • rodent • responsibilities • thundered • alas • muttered • dismay • outrage • intoned • disturbed • indisputable • consorts • indulged • disgust • obviously • wonder • deny • renounce • decency • assurance • commanding • distinctive • civilized • thudded • egregious • assembled • bellow • surged • marveled

CHAPTERS 11 TO 15
• ominous • courtly • retreated • burly • flawless • swoon • irritably • shuddered • contemplated • abyss • devotion • assumed • callused • beleaguered • cons • treacherous • monstrosity

CHAPTERS 16 TO 19
• prophecy • inordinate • confessor • contentment • chock-full • guarantees • gasped • cloak • intently • domain • despicable • torment • astute • solace • sympathetic • burden • tapestries • bedazzled • waltzed • minstrel • consigned

CHAPTERS 20 TO 23
• ornate • chandelier • admiring • spectacle • midst • merriment • unsavory • weeping • instrumental • revenge • banquet • lopsided • dire • consequence • indulge • tortuous • desperation • decreed • outlawed

CHAPTERS 24 TO 29
• billowing • enthusiasm • frequent • scrupulously • resemble • horizon • hut • innumerable • roundabout • grim • consume • aim • curtsy • thud • bold • destined • abundantly

CHAPTERS 30 TO 33
• plump • permeated • bungle • olfactory • stench • discernible • bellower • presumes • borne • ferocious • deliberate • portentous • acquaintance • ascertaining • aspirations • diabolical

CHAPTERS 34 TO 40
• miraculous • pondering • gratitude • covert • divine • comeuppance • constitute • understatement • annoyed • highness • sensibilities • defiant • ignorant • complicated • dappled • ceasing • empathy • riddance • rubbish • earnest

CHAPTERS 41 TO 46
• tapestry • cascading • diminishment • nearsighted • particle • audible • dismay • meditative • compelled • lair • perspective • beatific • emboldened • wafted • indicator • accustomed • devious • gusto • cornucopia

CHAPTERS 47 TO CODA
• surrender • humanity • thwarted • scaly • tufts • vengeful • infringe • consigned • anticipated • torment • atone

Kate DiCamillo

Just like in her books, Kate DiCamillo has traveled too. She was born on March 25 in Philadelphia, Pennsylvania. When she was five years old, along with her mother and her older brother, she moved to Clermont, Florida. Her health was fragile and the warm air would be better for her.

She attended College in Florida and even had a job at Walt Disney World in Florida. She moved more to the north to Minneapolis, Minnesota where she worked on the third floor of a second-hand bookstore.

She has always had a fascination with words and stories. She considers herself extremely lucky to be able to be a storyteller and write stories for a living.

Since the year 2000 she has been very busy. She has been honored and rewarded for her work. Her novel <u>Because of Winn-Dixie</u> won a Newbery Honor. Then, her following

book, <u>The Tiger Rising</u> was nominated for the National Book Award. Two years later <u>The Tale of Despereaux</u> received the Newbery Medal. Then, in 2005, <u>Because of Winn-Dixie</u> came out as a movie! Today she continues to write, tells stories, speaks to students and fellow writers.

Did You Know?

- **Kate lives and writes in Minneapolis, Minnesota.**
- **<u>The Tale of Despereaux</u> won the 2003 Newbery Award.**
- **Kate has no children of her own but she is an aunt to Luke, Roxanne and Max.**

NAME: _____

Chapters One to Five

1. Before you begin the novel, look at the cover of the book. What does it show? What does it suggest to you that the book might be about? Explain your answer.

_____

_____

2. Who do you think is the character, Despereaux? What kind of name is "Despereaux"? What do you think it stands for?

_____

_____

Vocabulary

Complete each sentence with a word from the list.

| maiden | adhere | squiggles | instincts | dungeon | proclaimed | shard |

1. The story is about a fair _____ and a knight who rescues her.

2. The mirror broke and I had a _____ of glass stuck in the sole of my shoe.

3. The pieces of sticky tape _____ very well to the paper.

4. "I have had enough. That's it!" _____ the upset mother.

5. Take him down to the _____ and lock him up!

6. His _____ were right; danger was around the corner.

7. For those who cannot read, words look like meaningless _____.

Chapters One to Five

Part A

1. **Circle T if the statement is TRUE or F if it is FALSE.**

   T F **a)** Despereaux was born with his eyes closed shut.

   T F **b)** He was named Despereaux because of all the despair in the home.

   T F **c)** He has a brother called Merlot and a sister called Furlough.

   T F **d)** Despereaux had the gift of reading.

   T F **e)** Mice who didn't conform were sent to the dungeon where rats lived.

   T F **f)** King Phillip was put to sleep by Princess Pea's guitar playing and singing.

2. **Number the events from ❶ to ❻ in the order they occurred in the chapters.**

   _____ **a)** The sound of King Phillip's music made Despereaux's soul grow large.

   _____ **b)** Despereaux fell in love with the princess.

   _____ **c)** The mother and father were disappointed only one mouse had survived.

   _____ **d)** Despereaux's health wasn't the best.

   _____ **e)** Despereaux sat on top of the king's foot.

   _____ **f)** Despereaux's sister brought him to eat books, but he preferred to read them.

Chapters One to Five

Part B

Answer each question with a complete sentence.

1. In Chapter One, we meet a mouse mother who gives her baby the name Despereaux. Why did she choose this name?

   _____

   _____

2. Despereaux is a very unusual mouse, with several peculiar characteristics. What about him, however, was most alarming of all?

   _____

   _____

3. Does this story remind you of any other story? Which one? Is it a fairy tale or a realistic story?

   _____

   _____

4. How and where did Despereaux learn to read?

   _____

   _____

5. If you were Furlough and Despereaux was your brother, what would your reaction have been when you saw your brother sitting on the king's foot?

   _____

   _____

Journal Activity

Imagine the excitement and anticipation the mouse mother and father would have felt before their babies were born. Write down your description. Then, describe their feelings when only one tiny and frail mouse survived whom they discovered did not act like a "normal" mouse.

Chapters Six to Ten

1. In Chapter Five, we read about the contact between Princess Pea and Despereaux. What awaits for them now? Will their relationships florish? Will there be any consequences? Explain.

   _____

   _____

2. There are advantages and disadvantages to having siblings. List two advantages and two disadvantages that you can think of (based on your own experience or using your imagination).

   _____

   _____

Vocabulary

Synonyms are words that have the same or similar meanings. Write each word from the list next to its synonym.

assurance	bellow	civilized	command	deny
despair	gaze	mutter	perfidy	statement

1. dictate _____

2. hopelessness _____

3. roar _____

4. look _____

5. confidence _____

6. treachery _____

7. mumble _____

8. affirmation _____

9. refined _____

10. renounce _____

Chapters Six to Ten

Part A

1. Put a check mark next to the answer that is most correct.

a) **How does Lester explain to Antoinette why Despereaux is the way he is?**

- ○ **A** He blames it on the birth.
- ○ **B** He blames Despereaux's siblings.
- ○ **C** He blames Despereaux's French roots.

b) **How was the tribunal called?**

- ○ **A** Lester hit the thimbal as a drum to call the tribunal.
- ○ **B** Lester whistled the tribunal.
- ○ **C** Lester called the tribunal on the phone.

c) **According to Princess Pea, what did Despereaux's ears feel like?**

- ○ **A** His ears felt like silk.
- ○ **B** His ears felt like satin.
- ○ **C** His ears felt like velvet.

d) **What did Despereaux say when he was sentenced to the dungeon?**

- ○ **A** He would not renounce his actions, but he loves his mother.
- ○ **B** He would not renounce his actions, but he loves the princess.
- ○ **C** He would not renounce his actions, but he loves his brother.

2. **Which answer best describes:**

a) Furlough?

- ○ **A** confused
- ○ **B** a really nice guy
- ○ **C** not very smart

b) Lester?

- ○ **A** strict
- ○ **B** gentil
- ○ **C** compassionate

c) Antoinette?

- ○ **A** over protective
- ○ **B** doesn't care
- ○ **C** understanding

d) Merlot?

- ○ **A** acts like a big sister
- ○ **B** acts like a baby
- ○ **C** acts like a grandmother

After You Read 📖

NAME: _____

Chapters Six to Ten

 Part B

Answer each question with a complete sentence.

1. Do you agree with Lester for turning in his son? Give good reasons for your answer.

_____

_____

2. Why do you think Antoinette didn't stop Lester?

_____

_____

3. Why was Lester so anxious to turn Despereaux in?

_____

_____

4. If you were Princess Pea, how would you try to guarantee Despereaux's safety?

_____

_____

5. What do you think is the worst thing that could happen to Despereaux? How did you come to that conclusion?

_____

_____

Journal Activity

Despereaux is headed for trouble – either with the Mouse Council and being sent to the dungeon, or falling in love with a princess. Write a short letter to Despereaux warning him of possible dangers ahead. What advice would you give him?

Chapters Eleven to Fifteen

1. What do you think will happen to Despereaux down in the dungeon? Why do you think he fainted?

_____

_____

_____

2. Why do you think people and rats were living downstairs in the dungeon together?

_____

_____

_____

Vocabulary

Across

4. To think and reflect deeply on a subject
5. To faint due to strong emotions (i.e. shock)
7. Dedication or strong attachment to a person, place or thing
9. Tremble violently
10. Strongly and heavily built; husky

Down

1. To cheat or trick someone
2. Perfect
3. To move back or away from a danger or challenge
6. Dignified and elegant manner
8. Easily annoyed

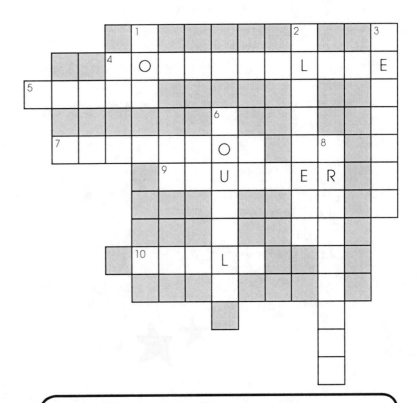

Word List
BURLY   DEVOTION   SHUDDER   CON
FLAWLESS   SWOON   CONTEMPLATE
IRRITABLE   COURTLY   RETREAT

Chapters Eleven to Fifteen

Part A

1. **Circle T if the statement is TRUE or F if it is FALSE.**

   T F **a)** The threadmaster told Despereaux to be brave for the princess.

   T F **b)** Despereaux fainted a second time during the council meeting.

   T F **c)** Antoinette's last words to Despereaux were "so long".

   T F **d)** One of the hoods who brought Despereaux to the dungeon was his own sister.

   T F **e)** Despereaux asked if he could see the princess one last time.

   T F **f)** Gregory, the jailer, would save Despereaux if Despereaux read him a story.

2. **Number the events from ① to ⑥ in the order they occurred in the chapters.**

   _____ **a)** Antoinette was worried about what was going to happen to her baby.

   _____ **b)** Despereaux wanted to be brave so he started to recite the story about the knight and his armor.

   _____ **c)** Despereaux met Gregory, the jailer, when Gregory lit the match.

   _____ **d)** *Perfidy* and *Pea* were the two words Despereaux retained during his flight.

   _____ **e)** Two mice wearing black hoods brought Despereaux to the dungeon.

   _____ **f)** Despereaux was threaded in red thread by the threadmaster.

Chapters Eleven to Fifteen

Part B

Answer each question with a complete sentence.

1. Do you believe that there is such a thing as *Happily Ever After*? Give good reasons for your answer.

_____

_____

2. How would you feel if you were in Despereaux's situation? Try to list five words that describe how you would feel.

_____

_____

3. What do you think about Despereaux's fate? Is it reasonable or unreasonable? Explain your answer.

_____

_____

4. If you were on the Mouse Council, what would your verdict be? Why?

_____

_____

5. In what ways does the setting of the story (time and place) make it interesting?

_____

_____

Journal Activity We have read what Furlough, Lester, Antoinette and Despereaux think. We don't know what the Most Very Honored Head Mouse thinks. Rewrite Despereaux's trail from the point of view of the Head Mouse. Include new details and evidence that only the Head Mouse would know. Will your verdict be the same? Why or why not?

Chapters Sixteen to Nineteen

Answer the questions in complete sentences.

1. What do you think might be special about a rat named **Chiaroscuro**? What does this name make you think of? What connection might this rat have with Despereaux?

_____

_____

2. Using a dictionary, find the meaning of the word **destiny**. Have you ever met someone and felt that it was destined to happen? Explain.

_____

_____

Vocabulary

Use a straight line to match each word to its definition. Use a dictionary to help you.

1	torment		a loose and sleeveless outer garment	A
2	chock-full		ready, witted and clever	B
3	consign		to utter breathlessly	C
4	astute		filled up completely	D
5	cloak		to worry or	E
6	gasp		to give over to the care of another	F

_____

_____

The Tale of Despereaux CC2302

Chapters Sixteen to Nineteen

Part A

1. **Answer questions with the words in the list.**

Roscuro	rope	red tablecloth	Botticelli Remorso	prisoner

a) What did Gregory own?

b) What is the name of the one-eared rat?

c) What had the prisoner traded his daughter for?

d) Who had the obsession with light?

e) Who had the astute powers of observation?

2. **Number the events from ❶ to ❺ in the order they occurred in the chapters.**

_____ **a)** Roscuro was inordinately interested in light because it gave meaning to life.

_____ **b)** Roscuro didn't really want the red cloth; he wanted the light behind it.

_____ **c)** Boticelli worked on Roscuro to be a "real" rat.

_____ **d)** The prisoner told Roscuro that he traded his daugher for the red tablecloth.

_____ **e)** Instead of torturing the prisoner, Roscuro encouraged the prisoner to tell all his inner secrets.

Chapters Forty-one to Forty-six

Answer the questions in complete sentences.

1. How do you think the Head Mouse will react when he finds out that Despereaux is still alive? What will the new plan be?

_____

_____

2. Using a dictionary, find the meaning of the word **quest**. Have you ever been on a quest? Where and when did this happen? Explain.

_____

_____

Vocabulary

Use a dictionary to find the meaning of each of the following words. Write each word next to its definition. In the boxes, write each word's part of speech (noun, verb, adjective, etc.).

audible	cascade	lair	perspective	tapestry	waft

	Word	Part of Speech	Meaning
1			point of view
2			float gently and easily
3			a rush of water
4			heavy hand-worked fabric
5			to be able to be heard
6			hideaway

NAME: _____

Chapters Forty-one to Forty-six

Part A

Circle T if the statement is TRUE or F if it is FALSE.

T F **a)** Despereaux found the King crying and sitting on the Princess' bed.

T F **b)** The King fully understood what Despereaux was trying to do.

T F **c)** The threadmaster called Despereaux his friend.

T F **d)** Despereaux had to go through the kitchen to get to the dungeon.

T F **e)** After some good soup, Despereaux was ready to confront the dark dungeon.

T F **f)** Despereaux opened the dungeon door and tumbled all the way down the stairs.

2.   Complete the paragraph with the correct words from the story.

Despereaux was filled with _____. He found the _____ to tell
                    a   b

him about the _____ and where she was held captive in the _____.
             c   d

The King _____ and he didn't believe Despereaux. Despereaux knew he had
            e

to do something, so he went to the _____ to get some _____. Now he
                  f   g

could go into the _____ and find his way through the _____. Before he
              h   i

got to the _____, he was caught in the _____ by the _____.
         j   k   l

Together, they ate _____. The cook opened the _____ and down went
             m   n

Despereaux to save his _____.
             o

Chapters Forty-one to Forty-six

Part B

Answer the questions in complete sentences.

1. Why did the King refuse to listen to Despereaux when Despereaux was trying to tell him where the Princess was?

_____

_____

2. What led the threadmaster to say to Despereaux, "You, friend, are on a quest"?

_____

_____

3. Why do you think Hovis was in favor of Despereaux's quest? If you had been the threadmaster, what would you have done? Explain your answer.

_____

_____

4. In Chapter Forty-six, Botticelli refers to the spool of thread saying, "What a cornucopia of scents". What does he mean by this?

_____

_____

5. At the end of Chapter forty-six, Botticelli thinks to himself, "Just when you think that life in the dungeon cannot get any better, a mouse arrives". How would a mouse make things better from his perspective?

_____

_____

Journal Activity

> It seems there are more than two characters in this novel who are not the "sharpest knife in the drawer". Make a list of all the characters in this story, and write their names in order from the "dullest" to the "sharpest". Then, make a second list, putting them in order from the kindest to the cruelest. Compare your answers with a friend.

Chapter Forty-seven to Coda

1. How do you think the rats will capture Despereaux? Do you think they will harm him?

_____

_____

2. How could Despereaux have gone into the dungeon better prepared? How could he convince the King and the cook to follow him downstairs?

_____

_____

Vocabulary

Across

1. To defeat
4. Expect
7. Seeking revenge
8. A feeling of sadness, misery or sorrow
9. Great surprise or wonder
10. Treat cruelly

Down

2. Quality or state of being human
3. Covered with hard and bumpy skin
5. To violate, trespass, go beyond recognised bounds
6. To give over to trust or care of another

Word List

AMAZEMENT	HUMANITY	TORMENT
ANTICIPATE	INFRINGE	VENGEFUL
CONSIGN	SCALY	GLOOM
THWART		

Chapter Forty-seven to Coda

Part A

1. Number the events from **1** to **5** in the order they occurred in the chapters.

_____ **a)** Hanging onto his tail, Despereaux followed Botticelli to the Princess.

_____ **b)** The jailer who sold his daughter was released from the dungeon.

_____ **c)** Despereaux and Botticelli become somewhat friends.

_____ **d)** Roscuro tells Mig that no one cares about what she wants.

_____ **e)** Mig admits she misses her Ma and as does the Princess.

2. Do you agree or disagree with the statements below? Circle your answers, and be ready to justify your opinions.

Agree   Disagree   **a)** In real life, people can live "happily ever after".

Agree   Disagree   **b)** This story was not realistic in any way.

Agree   Disagree   **c)** I believe in fate and destiny.

Agree   Disagree   **d)** When you have a dream, go for it.

Chapter Forty-seven to Coda

Part B

1. Which character did you find most interesting (whether you liked them or not)? Explain your answer.

   _____

   _____

   _____

2. Are you satisfied with the ending of the story? Did it turn out the way you thought or hoped it would? Give good reasons for your answers.

   _____

   _____

   _____

3. If you could join in the cast of characters in this novel, who would you be? What would your character be like? How would you fit into the story?

   _____

   _____

   _____

4. Did you enjoy the moments in the novel when the author interrupted the story to address you (as the reader)? Did this give you a better understanding of the story? Was her approach effective?

   _____

   _____

   _____

Journal Activity

Reread Chapter Forty-nine. At the end of the chapter, the author tells us that the mouse will arrive on scene. Write a new ending for the story, continuing on from the end of this chapter. What will you change? What will happen to Despereaux? Ruscuro? The Princess? Mig? Will your ending be more tragic, more frightening, or more funny? Be creative.

Chapters 1 to 5

<u>The Tale of Despereaux</u> begins with the birth of a mouse, the main character of this novel, Despereaux. Do you know what happened when you were born? **Your task is to write the first chapter of your life.**

First, write down **eight to ten interview questions** to ask one of your parents, grandparents, or another family member who was present when you were born. Find out as much information as you can about this time.

Here are some questions you may wish to ask in your interview:

- How was your name chosen?
- How did your siblings respond to your arrival?
- What news event happened when you were born?

Then, take all the information from your interview and write the first chapter in

<u>The Tale of</u> _____!

Chapters 6 to 15

Despereaux has gone into the dungeon, far away from his family and friends. Surprisingly, when his parents return to their little home they find a letter that Despereaux has left for them!

Your task is to write the letter that Despereaux left for his mother and father.

What do you think he might have written? Is the letter comical? Is it sentimental? Perhaps it is apologetic. Think about what he would want to say to his parents (and maybe his siblings, too). What lasting memory did he write about?

Use the proper friendly letter format that you have learned.
Be sure to include the date and sign it with Despereaux's signature.
Your letter should be at least one half-page in length.

Bonus: Remember that Despereaux's parents could not read! Explain what they would need to do to find out what Despereaux had written in his letter.

Chapters 16 to 23

In these chapters, we follow Roscuro's exciting adventure in the banquet hall, from swinging on the chandelier, to the Queen falling over dead. The King, heartbroken by the Queen's death, outlaws rats, soup and all the instruments need to both make and eat soup!

Your task is to write a radio announcement for the King,
telling the population about the new regulations.

Here are some questions for you to think about:
- What will your message say?
- What tone will your message have?
- What consequences will there be for anyone who does not obey the King's rules?

Once you have written your announcement, practice reading it aloud. Be sure to speak clearly and not too fast so that your listeners can understand your message. Then, perform your announcement for your classmates.

- -

Chapters 24 to 33

In *Book The Third* we meet Miggery Sow and learn about her horrible, and very unfortunate childhood. She is not, however, the only character in this story who had a terrible childhood – both Despereaux and Roscuro did, too.

For this activity you will compare the childhoods of these three characters with your own life so far.

Create a chart with four columns. Write the names, "Miggery Sow", "Despereaux" and "Roscuro" at the top of the first three columns. The fourth column is for your name. Write down details about the childhood years of each character and your own. What are the similarities? Where are the differences?

If you could change the events and circumstances of either Mig's, Despereaux's or Roscuro's childhood, which would you change? What would be different?

Chapter 34 to Coda

Imagine that you are in the middle of a natural disaster such as a fire, an earthquake or a flood. All of the characters in <u>The Tale of Despereaux</u> are caught in the disaster with you. Fortunately, you realize that you can save yourself and *one other creature* (human or animal). You decide to rescue one of the characters from the story! Which one will you choose?

> **Your task is to write about this scene.**
>
> **Describe the natural disaster and the destruction it makes. Then, tell about which character's life you will save, and why you chose him or her in particular. You will also need to describe how you went about saving this character's life.**

- -

 Writing Task # 6

Chapter 34 to Coda

Imagine that you are a librarian, and it is your job to recommend a novel for <u>The Book of Month</u>. You have chosen Kate DiCamillo's <u>The Tale of Despereaux</u>.

> **Your task is to create a poster to promote this novel.**
> Your poster should have a catchy title, and be colorful so that others will want to read the book.

To help get students excited about reading the novel, you will need to include a summary of the story *without revealing the ending!* Your summary should be one paragraph in length, and be sure to make it interesting. An excellent book should have an excellent summary! Be neat and creative!

NAME: _____

Word Search

Find all of the words in the Word Search. Words may be horizontal, vertical or even diagonal. A few may even be backwards. Look carefully!

brilliance	outrage	chandelier	defiant
dungeon	shuddered	consequence	complicated
maiden	flawless	resemble	wafted
velvet	inordinate	frequent	nearsighted
rodent	gasped	horizon	squint
furiously	cloak	ferocious	proclaim
wonder	banquet	stench	bellow

a	h	s	u	d	e	t	a	c	i	l	p	m	o	c	s	u	h
t	o	f	i	n	o	r	d	i	n	a	t	e	g	e	v	n	e
r	r	u	l	e	n	l	a	r	d	e	r	e	d	d	u	h	s
b	e	o	i	e	c	u	r	s	w	l	o	n	i	o	f	s	u
a	r	f	d	q	f	u	r	i	o	u	s	l	y	e	r	a	o
s	e	i	d	e	s	e	r	t	n	o	o	y	n	m	e	r	i
u	a	l	l	h	n	o	a	e	d	l	e	r	c	i	q	g	c
m	s	l	a	l	u	t	s	t	e	n	c	h	h	a	u	o	o
e	n	m	i	t	i	p	i	c	r	v	t	a	a	l	e	i	r
s	e	e	r	d	u	a	s	h	o	n	g	m	n	c	n	b	e
e	q	a	w	e	a	s	n	w	a	f	t	e	d	o	t	r	f
s	g	u	m	m	g	s	t	c	d	s	t	h	e	r	b	u	l
e	n	a	i	l	p	e	l	i	e	h	c	s	l	p	j	t	i
i	r	r	r	n	u	h	o	r	i	z	o	n	i	m	s	s	c
f	u	d	e	q	t	u	z	t	e	w	n	c	e	f	q	i	d
v	l	e	n	s	j	b	p	r	n	i	s	k	r	a	m	u	e
e	h	a	w	r	e	f	v	p	r	h	e	i	m	i	n	t	f
n	b	a	w	c	w	m	s	q	c	s	q	v	f	g	r	g	i
t	b	e	l	l	o	w	b	o	i	o	u	i	e	o	s	p	a
i	r	n	d	o	e	t	n	l	n	o	e	o	p	l	s	e	n
o	a	s	e	a	p	s	g	d	e	l	n	p	o	n	v	t	t
n	h	g	n	k	g	a	s	p	e	d	c	a	r	a	t	e	u
t	p	n	e	a	r	s	i	g	h	t	e	d	a	m	i	l	t